Ultimate Sticker Collection

Penguin
Random
House

Written and edited by **Julia March**
Designed by **Jessica Tapolcai** and **Lynne Moulding**
Cover designed by **Lisa Robb** and **Lynne Moulding**

First published in Great Britain in 2019 by
Dorling Kindersley Limited
80 Strand, London WC2R 0RL
A Penguin Random House Company

10 9 8 7 6 5 4 3 2 1
001–314133–Feb/2019

A CIP catalogue record for this book is available from the British Library.

ISBN: 978-0-24137-796-3

Printed and bound in China

www.dk.com
www.fingerlings.com

A WORLD OF IDEAS:
SEE ALL THERE IS TO KNOW

How to use this book

Read the captions, then find the sticker that best fits the space.
(Hint: check the sticker labels for clues!)

•

There are lots of fantastic extra stickers, too!

MEET THE FINGERLINGS

Welcome to Melody Village, home of the Fingerlings. These monkeys, sloths and unicorns are the funniest animals ever – and the friendliest, too!

Unicorns

Life is sweet for Gigi and her unicorn pals. They live in Sparkle Heights, where everything is made of sweets.

Sloths

Sloths Marge and Kingsley live at Sloth Beach. They like to relax and take things slow... really, really slow.

Monkeys

The monkeys are bouncy, cheeky and lots of fun. They live in the Vines, high up in the treetops.

Going bananas!
There is one thing the monkeys like even more than swinging in the treetops. They just love bananas!
Monkey leaders
Twins Bella and Boris lead the monkeys in their madcap games. They live in a treetop hut.
Fingerling friends
From their homes all over Melody Village, the Fingerlings get together for fun every day.
Hello, Fingerlings. Thanks for inviting us to Melody Village!

CHEEKY MONKEYS

The monkeys can drive the other Fingerlings bananas with their antics, but they don't mean any harm. They just want to have fun – and making mischief is a lot of fun!

Bella

Bella is the twin of Boris. This bright pink monkey is kind and loving. She takes all Boris's noisy antics in her stride!

Boris

Boisterous, blue-furred Boris is the noisiest monkey of all. He talks non-stop, and plays the drums, too.

Finn

Finn is a fun-loving black monkey who is always on the go. Fast Finn always wins in a game of chase!

Zoe

When Zoe wants to take a banana break, she hangs upside down by her long, curly turquoise tail.

Mia

Mia is a purple monkey who is into everything. Curious Mia wants to know all about the great big world around her.

Sophie

Sophie is a white monkey who loves to dance. She hops, spins and shimmies on her hands as well as on her feet.

MAGICAL UNICORNS

The unicorns love drama. They prance and swish their manes wherever they go. Glitter and sweets are their favourite things. Glittery sweets are even better!

Gigi

Gigi is simply unforgettable! She is the sparkliest, chattiest and most flamboyant of the unicorns by far.

Gemma

Gemma's pink coat looks like sweet strawberry icing. That suits her, since she is a very sweet unicorn.

Skye

Skye uses her special unicorn magic to fly in the sky, high above the candyfloss clouds of Sparkle Heights.

Stella
Dreamy Stella likes to gaze at the sky and make wishes on shooting stars. Sometimes her wishes come true!
Molly
Molly's favourite colour is rose gold. She is very happy that her unicorn horn is that pretty colour. Well, almost!
Alika
Everyone knows when Alika has been near. This purple unicorn always leaves a sprinkle of magic in her trail.
How beautiful you are, unicorns. Just look at those rainbow manes and tails!

SLEEPY SLOTHS

The sloths are definitely not fans of hustle and bustle. They live a slow-paced, surfer lifestyle on Sloth Beach. But don't call them lazy – they are just laid-back!

Marge

Marge loves exploring (at her own pace). She wears a backpack and a hat with her pet bug perched on top.

Books, bugs and bedtime

Marge likes books. She likes bugs, too. And she loves reading books about bugs before bed!

Surfing sloth

When he isn't hanging on a branch, Kingsley hangs ten on a surfboard. After all that action, he soon needs a snooze!

Kingsley

Kingsley spends a lot of time relaxing. If you ask him how he has spent his day, he will tell you "just hangin', dude"!

Funny faces

Kingsley does funny, goofy things all the time. He likes to pull silly faces to make his friends laugh.

Feeling hangry!

Sometimes, Marge goes exploring and forgets to take a snack. Being hangry takes her from calm to crabby!

IN THE VINES

It's very quiet in the Vines today. Time to liven things up! Find some Fingerlings from the extra stickers and create your own treetop scene.

BELLA AND BORIS

For twins, Bella and Boris are not alike. Bella keeps fit and eats healthy foods, while Boris loves rock music and sugary cereal! Yet they are so close that they even have their own language.

Beloved Bella

There is no Fingerling more popular than Bella. She never forgets to tell her friends how much she loves them.

Banana boy

Boris eats two bowls of sugary cereal for breakfast. If he's still hungry, he snacks on tasty bananas.

Gym monkey

Bella is a keen gymnast who trains very hard. She holds the Fingerlings record for "most bounces in a single day".

Quiet moment

Shhh... Boris is having a rare quiet moment. He doesn't want to scare away this shy little butterfly.

Sing and swing
Boris burns off excess energy by swinging on a vine and singing his favourite rock song... very, very loudly!
Curious Bella
Bella is is a very curious monkey. She always asks her friends what they are up to. Maybe she can join in the fun!
If only we could understand monkey latin. Then we'd know what you are saying, twins!

GIGI

Gigi is a fabulous, fun-loving unicorn who is into selfies, scrapbooking and socialising. She always tries to make sure her friends are having fun, but she can be a teensy bit bossy!

Everyone's friend

Gigi has dozens of friends, and would love to have even more. She thinks of her friends as her "fam".

Sweet lover

This sweet unicorn loves sweets, especially lollies. Luckily, lollies grow like trees in Sparkle Heights!

Heart on her sleeve

Gigi doesn't believe in hiding her emotions. When she is extra happy, everyone in Melody Village knows it!

Dancing unicorn

When Gigi hears music, she just has to get up and dance. She swooshes her rainbow mane in time to the music.

Oops!

Sometimes, Gigi gets carried away and does something silly. She once spun Marge round so fast she flew into the sky!

Selfies

Gigi is always taking selfies. She has a range of cute facial expressions, including her unicorn pout.

We'd love to take your photo, Gigi. Are you ready for a close-up?

BANANA SHACK

In the daytime, the Banana Shack serves tasty banana-based snacks. At night, it hosts hilarious comedy shows. Anyone is welcome to step up and have a try at tickling their fellow Fingerlings' funnybones!

Comedy timing

It's all in the timing! Mia keeps the audience waiting for a moment before delivering her funny punch line.

Ho ho, Zoe!

Zoe finds the way Marge tells jokes really funny. In fact, sometimes she laughs so hard she simply can't stop.

Bella's debut

It's Bella's first time at the mike, and she's nervous. Will she forget one of her jokes? Will Boris try to heckle her?

Sloth support

When Marge steps up to the mike, Kingsley cheers and waves (rather slowly) to show his support.

Unicorny jokes!

Gigi tells really corny jokes at the comedy sessions. Sometimes she even makes herself laugh, they are so silly.

Funny crowd

Sometimes, the audience tries to get a performer to laugh by making silly faces. It can be funnier than the joke!

Shhhh... quiet, everyone. Marge is ready to start her comedy routine.

SELFIE SHOW

Gigi likes to capture her many moods by taking selfies. Can you find the right stickers to go with the moods on these five mobile phone screens?

KISSY
SILLY
BASHFUL
SURPRISED

GET HAPPY!

Nothing gets the Fingerlings down for long. They believe in being positive and staying happy. If you hang out with the Fingerlings, you'll soon be feeling happy too!

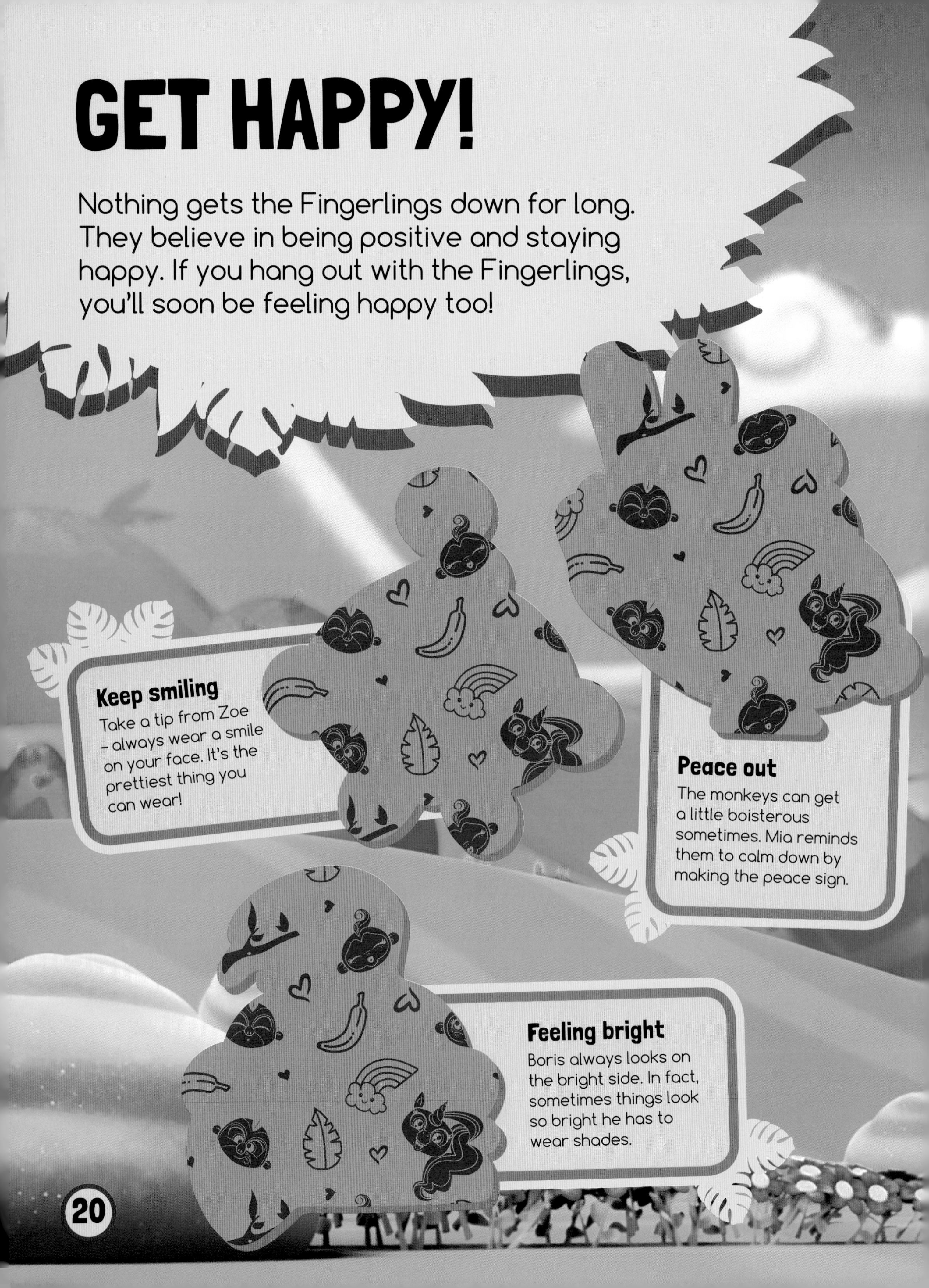

Keep smiling

Take a tip from Zoe – always wear a smile on your face. It's the prettiest thing you can wear!

Peace out

The monkeys can get a little boisterous sometimes. Mia reminds them to calm down by making the peace sign.

Feeling bright

Boris always looks on the bright side. In fact, sometimes things look so bright he has to wear shades.

Look for the rainbow
Dark skies and storm clouds don't bother Gigi. She knows it won't be long before a lovely rainbow will appear.
Thanks for being our friend, Gigi. You make everyone happy!
Thumbs up!
When something makes Kingsley happy, he gives it the thumbs up sign. A tasty leaf taco earns a double thumbs up.
Happy to share
A gift of sweets can get anyone smiling. Gemma is always happy to share her treats with her pals.

TIME FOR FUN

In Melody Village, the fun goes on from dawn until dusk. There is always time for fun!

Monkey racer

The monkeys love to race each other to win prizes. Fast Finn often takes first prize – usually a banana.

Pamper time

Fun doesn't always mean action. The unicorns often get together to gossip and to share mane styling tips.

Bubble up

Blowing bubbles is a fun way to spend an hour. Bella tries to make each of her bubbles bigger than the last.

Surfing Marge
When Marge feels more wide-awake than usual, she borrows Kingsley's surfboard for an hour.
In the swing
Swinging from vine to vine is Mia's idea of fun, especially if her monkey friends join in with the acrobatics.
Wake up, Eddie! The fun and games have already started!
Let's dance
If one Fingerling starts dancing, everyone else will soon join in. They all agree – the more the merrier.

MORE MONKEYS

The Glitter Girls put the melody into Melody Village as they sparkle, swing and sweetly sing. Not like the Minis! These tiny terrors ambush other Fingerlings and steal their treats.

Mean Mini

This mean Mini is always on the lookout for bananas. If he sees a Fingerling with one, he leads his pals in a whirlwind attack.

Cheeky Mini

Teasing Boris (after stealing his banana) is this Mini's favourite hobby. He makes sure he is out of Boris's reach first!

Amelia

With her blue colour and myriad sparkles, Amelia looks just like the stars have come out in the daytime sky!

Rose

This cute Glitter Girl monkey keeps her friends tickled pink with her funny jokes and pranks.

Kiki

Purple is Kiki's colour. She looks just like a pretty violet in a garden, but of course much, much sparklier.

Keep singing, Sugar – your voice is as sweet as can be!

Sugar

Sugar is just like icing on a special party cake – sweet, white and very sparkly.

PLAYTIME PUZZLE

The monkeys want to play on their see-saw and monkey bars, but everything is in pieces. Can you find the parts and put together the equipment?

The monkey bars have a climbing frame, a swing and Liv the monkey.

Milly and Willy play all day on their purple see-saw. Up, down, up, down...

FRIENDS FOREVER

Friends make good times better and bad times not quite so bad! Melody Village is filled with Fingerling friends, all sharing hopes, dreams, laughs and hugs.

Hug it out

If you fall out with a friend, don't stay cross. Talk it over and then hug it out, like Sophie and Mia.

Best friends

A best friend is a special, close friend. Bella and Mia are best friends, and share all their secrets.

Opposites attract

Friends don't have to be alike. Fast Finn gets along just fine with slow sloths Kingsley and Marge.

Gigi's family

Gigi loves her friends so much that she thinks of them as family. She even calls them her "fam"!

Be our friend!

Don't forget, the Fingerlings want to be your friend, too. In Melody Village, everyone is welcome.

Why are you giggling, Fingerling friends? Can we share your joke?

GIGI'S PARTY

Gigi is having a party, and she has invited everyone in Melody Village! Find some guests among the extra stickers and create a perfect party scene.

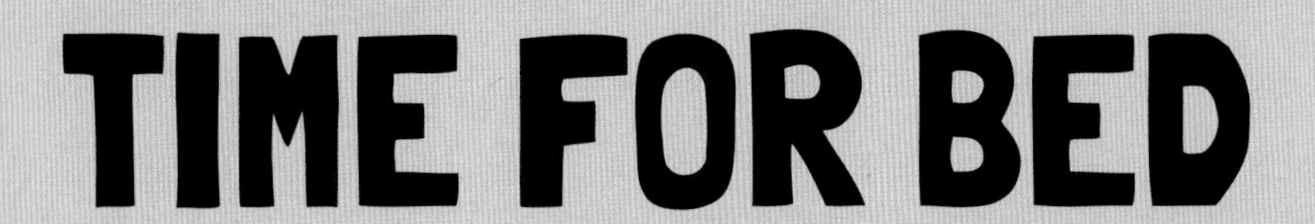

TIME FOR BED

At the end of a fun-filled day it can be hard to say goodnight to your friends and go to bed. But everyone needs to sleep eventually – even Fingerlings.

Sleepy sloth

Kingsley is happy to go to bed (even though he has been napping all day!).

Bedtime tears

Boohoo! Gigi doesn't want to go to bed. She wishes her lovely day could go on forever.

Goodnight, everyone!

It's time for the Fingerlings to kiss goodnight, go to bed and close their eyes. See you tomorrow!

Sweet dreams, Zoe! We'll try not to wake you until morning.